WHAT MAKES THE SUN SHINE?

WHAT MAKES THE SUN SHINE?

ISAAC ASIMOV

ILLUSTRATIONS BY MARC BROWN

An Atlantic Monthly Press Book

Little, Brown and Company

BOSTON   TORONTO

To Emilie W. McLeod

WHAT MAKES THE SUN SHINE?

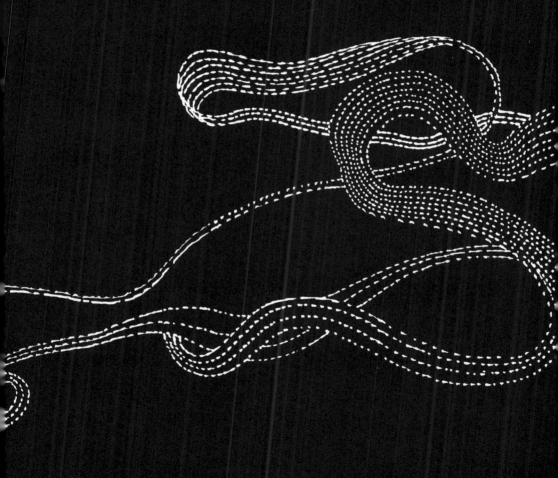

Once upon a time, about six billion years ago, there were no Sun and no Earth. Instead there was a very large cloud of gas that slowly turned round and round. It was at least ten billion miles across.

Where did all that huge cloud of gas come from? Nobody really knows for sure, but it was there.

The cloud of gas was surrounded by many billion miles of nothing at all.

Why did the cloud of gas not spread out into the nothingness? It ought to have gotten thin-

ner and thinner and thinner and finally become so thin it might as well be nothing.

It didn't happen that way. Each part of the gas attracted all the other parts. The attraction is called *gravitation*. The parts of the cloud of gas were held together by gravitation, just as you are held to the Earth.

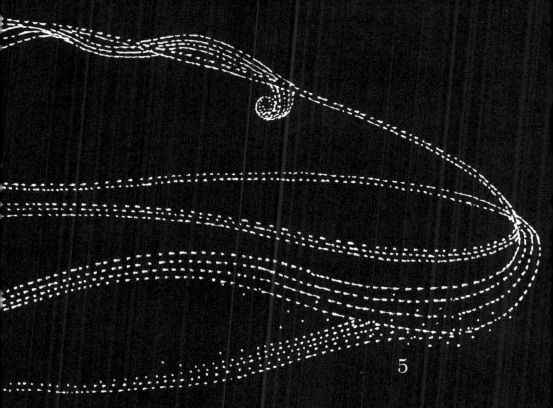

If you jump up from the ground, you drop down again. That is gravitation pulling you. The Earth's pull is pretty strong because all the material in it is crowded into one large ball.

The gas cloud of billions of years ago had its material spread out over billions of miles. The gravitation pull was spread out, too, so that it was weak.

But even though it was weak, it was there!

It was strong enough to keep the gas cloud from spreading out into empty space. Gravitational pull held the gas cloud together. In fact, it kept pulling it closer and closer together.

Each little bit of the gas cloud was dropping toward the center of the cloud. It was doing it just as surely as you would drop toward the Earth if you jumped off a wall.

The gravitational pull in the gas cloud was so weak that the parts of the cloud pulled to-

gether only very slowly. It kept on pulling slowly together for a million years or so.

The more it pulled together, the more the gravitational pull was concentrated and the stronger it got. The gas cloud pulled together faster and faster until finally, it came tightly together to form the Sun.

What happened to the cloud of gas as it pulled together?

For one thing, the way it turned changed.

The cloud was turning to begin with, but very slowly. It may have taken the big original cloud of gas millions of years to turn around even once.

Why it was turning in the first place, no one really knows. But it was. And once it was turning it had to keep on turning. There was no way of getting rid of the turning motion.

As the cloud of gas pulled together, it turned

through a smaller and smaller distance. The smaller distance reduced the turning motion. To make up for that, the turning had to be faster and faster.

By the time the cloud had gotten quite small, maybe only a few million miles across, it was spinning very fast. It was spinning so fast that some of the gas was thrown off in the middle and spread out into a flat sheet.

The gas in the flat sheet swirled about and clung together. Finally, it settled into large clumps. Those clumps are the nine planets that still move in a big spin about the Sun. The Earth is one of those planets. It is 93 million miles from the Sun and it moves about it once a year.

Some planets, like Mars and Jupiter, formed farther away from the Sun than the Earth did. Some, like Venus and Mercury, formed closer

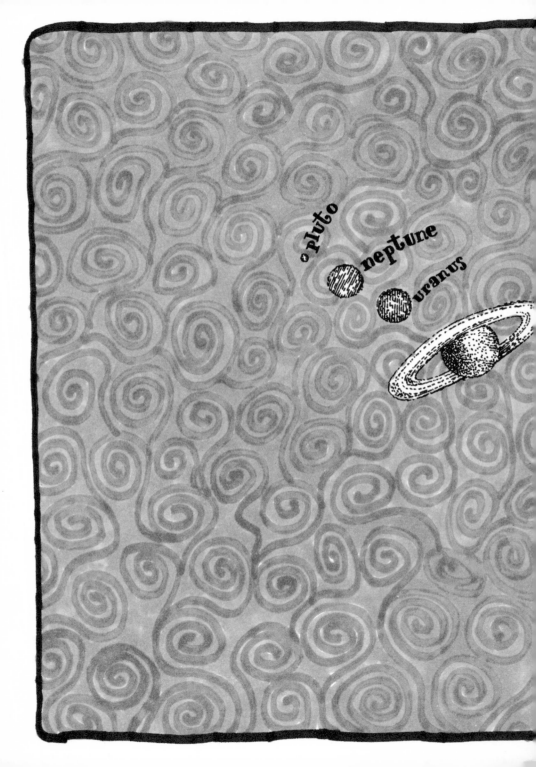

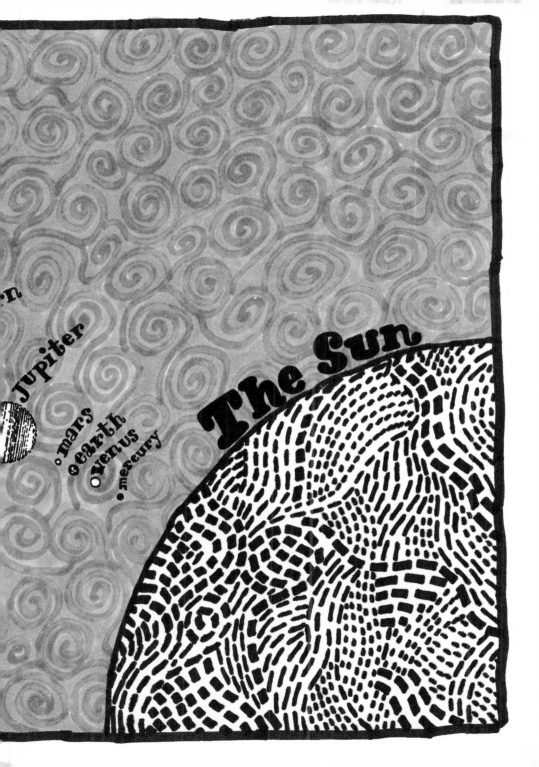

to the Sun. Some planets, like Jupiter, are much larger than the Earth; some, like Mercury, are smaller.

There is one thing about all the planets, though. They don't shine.

We see the planets in the sky like dots of light, but that is not their own light. We actually see the sunlight striking them and bouncing off them.

The Moon only shines because sunlight is bouncing off it. When we see a half-moon, that is because only half the part we see is in sunlight. The rest is not getting any sunlight, so it is dark and we don't see it.

The Sun, however, shines of its own light. Light is always streaming out of it. Light has been streaming out of it for billions of years and will keep on doing so for billions of more years.

Why is the Sun so different from the planets? What makes the Sun shine?

For one thing, the Sun is much larger than the planets. Most of the original cloud of gas pulled together to form the Sun. Very little of it spread out into a flat sheet to make the planets.

There is 750 times more matter in the Sun than in all the planets put together.

Let's see what difference this makes.

Did you ever notice that when something falls, it moves faster and faster as it falls? If you're not sure about this, try an experiment. Have a friend hold a baseball a foot over your hand and then drop it so you can catch it. Then have him hold the same baseball out of a second-story window and drop it, not throw it, so you can catch it.

The ball falls for a longer time before you catch it when it is dropped out of a second-story window. You know it is moving faster then by how it feels when you catch it.

That is why it is so dangerous for a person to fall from a high window. He has time to fall faster and hit the ground harder.

The same thing holds true for the bits of gas that are falling together toward the center of the cloud. As they fall, they gradually move faster and faster and faster till they come together in a tight ball.

14

How fast they end up going depends on how far they fall. It also depends on how much matter is falling together. The more matter there is, the stronger the gravitational pull. The stronger the gravitational pull, the faster everything falls.

The cloud of matter that formed the Earth fell together faster and faster. By the time the Earth came together as a solid ball, the bits of matter that made it up were moving very fast.

Jupiter is larger than the Earth. Its gravitational pull is stronger. By the time it formed, the bits of matter making it up were moving much faster than the bits making up the Earth.

The Sun is far larger still. Its gravitational

pull is much stronger than that of any planet. For that reason, the bits of matter making up the Sun came to move far faster than any of the matter making up any of the planets.

Does it matter how fast bits of matter move?

Yes, for matter that moves contains *energy*. The faster something moves, the more energy it has. The more energy it has the more it can do to other things.

For instance, suppose you touch a baseball to a windowpane and just hold it there. The baseball isn't moving. It has no energy of motion. It doesn't do anything to the window.

Suppose you move the baseball *very* slowly and hit the window with it. You will hear the

little noise it makes when it touches the window, but nothing will happen. The ball has a little energy but not enough to do anything to the window.

Next, suppose you throw the ball quite hard against the window. You know what will happen. The ball will be moving quickly. It will have a good deal of energy. And it will break that window!

Energy can be found in many different forms. We feel it, in one form, as *heat*.

When bits of matter move about and hit each other, they have a certain amount of energy in the form of heat. The faster they move about and the harder they hit each other, the more heat they have and the hotter they are.

The bits of matter that formed the Earth were moving so fast that the Earth was very hot when it first came together. Right now the outside of the Earth has cooled down. We can live on it for it never gets much hotter than 100° F. (°F. stands for degrees Fahrenheit) at most. It is much hotter inside the Earth. At the very center of the Earth, the temperature may be as much as 2700° F.

Jupiter, because it is larger and has greater gravitational pull, was even hotter than the Earth when it first formed. On the outside it has cooled down more than the Earth, because Jupiter is farther from the Sun. There is less heat reaching it from the Sun to keep Jupiter's outside warm. The center of Jupiter, however, is probably much hotter than the center of the Earth.

The Sun with its still greater gravitational pull must be hotter still. In fact, scientists think that at the very center of the Sun, the temperature may be as high as 25,000,000° F.

When the center is that hot, enough heat leaks out to keep even the outside of the Sun at a high temperature. The outside of the Sun is at a temperature of about 10,000° F.

Even the outside of the Sun is much hotter than the very center of the Earth.

When a piece of matter contains energy in the form of heat, some of that energy leaks out into the space all around. It leaks out in the form of waves. These waves coming out in all directions are called *radiation*.

When the temperature is low, the waves are very long and don't have much energy. We don't feel them.

The higher the temperature gets, the shorter the waves are, and the more energy they have. Pretty soon we begin to feel them.

Think of an electric iron which is used to press clothes. When it is not being used, it is just at the temperature of the room, perhaps about 70° F. At that temperature, it is radiating very long waves. You can't feel them. If you put your hand a few inches away from the iron, you feel nothing.

But suppose you plug the iron into the wall and turn on the electricity. The iron begins to get hotter. The waves it radiates get shorter and contain more energy. Pretty soon the iron

is quite hot. If you put your hand a few inches away from the flat surface of the iron, you can feel the heat. The waves radiating from that surface have enough energy to be felt by your hand.

Suppose something continues to get even hotter. By the time the temperature reaches about 1000° F. the waves that are radiated get so short and contain so much energy that they begin to affect the eye. Then you can see the radiation.

An electric iron never gets that hot. The coils on an electric stove do, though. If you have an electric stove and turn one of the coils on high, it will begin to grow hot. Soon it will be so hot, it will start to shine a dim red. Then it is *red hot*.

If something got hotter still, the light would get brighter and brighter. If it got hot enough, the light it would give off would turn orange, then yellow, then white.

The coil on an electric stove never gets hot enough to be *white hot*, but the wire in a strong electric light bulb does.

Anything at a high temperature would glow with light. The central part of the Earth is hot enough to shine. That shine is hidden by the cold outside of the planet.

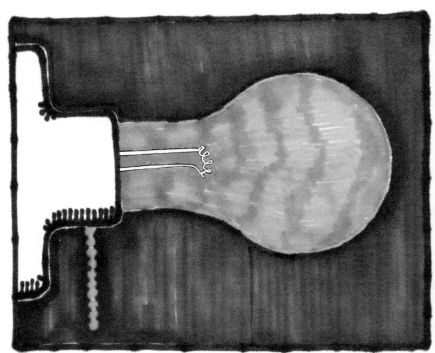

You see, then, what must have happened as the huge cloud of gas slowly pulled together to form the Sun. As it pulled together, it grew warmer and warmer. There finally came a point when it got small enough and hot enough to glow a very dim red.

About that time, the Earth was forming, too. If you could have been on the Earth and watched the Sun it would have been like seeing a great big ball in the sky, very dim, very deep red, with hazy edges.

While the surface of the Earth was cooling off, the Sun would continue pulling together. It would grow smaller and hotter. Its light would get brighter and more orange. It would get still brighter and brighter. It would turn yellow, then white.

About five billion years ago, the Sun would have looked very much as it does now. All these

billions of years it has been radiating light, the light we see by. It also sends out infrared radiation which has so little energy we can't see it. We can feel its heat, though. The Sun also sends out ultraviolet radiation which has too much energy to see. It can give us a suntan or a sunburn, however.

But there is a problem. Is there enough heat piled up through that pulling together to keep the Sun shining for five billion years?

If all the Sun's energy came from the pulling together of the original cloud of gas there would be only enough energy to keep it shining for a few hundred million years.

This is a long time but it is not enough. The Sun needs at least ten times as much energy as that. But where does the extra energy come from?

To answer that question, we must consider what the original cloud of gas was made of.

All matter is made up of tiny particles called *atoms*, which are far too small to see with even the best microscopes. Scientists have made careful experiments, however, and that makes them sure the atoms are there, even if they can't be seen.

There are over a hundred different kinds of atoms known. Some are very rare. Some are quite common.

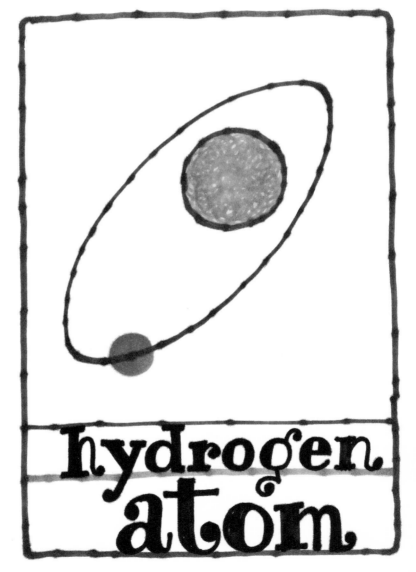

hydrogen atom

The simplest and smallest of all the atoms is the *hydrogen atom.* The next simplest and smallest is the *helium atom.*

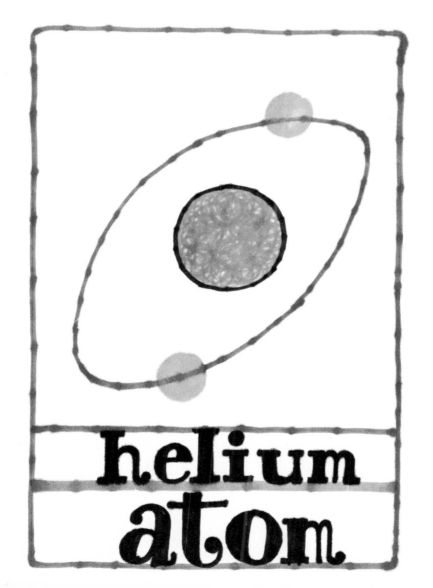

helium atom

Scientists have decided that about nine-tenths of all the atoms in the universe are hydrogen. Almost all the rest are helium. All the other kinds of atoms put together make up less than one-hundredth of the total.

When the Earth formed, only the more complicated atoms were pulled together. The Earth is mostly made up of atoms of oxygen, iron, sulfur, magnesium, aluminum and so on. There is only a little bit of hydrogen on the Earth and almost no helium.

This is because hydrogen and helium atoms are so small it is hard for the gravitational pull to hold them. The gravitational pull of the Earth was too small to hold the hydrogen and helium.

Jupiter's gravitational pull is larger. It contains a large amount of hydrogen and helium.

The Sun's gravitational pull is still larger.

Most of the original cloud of gas was hydrogen and helium and nearly all of it came together to form the Sun.

Let's think about the hydrogen and helium. Chemists use abbreviations for them. They let H stand for hydrogen and He for helium.

The helium atoms are very standoffish. Each helium atom stays by itself. The hydrogen atoms are different. They cling together in pairs. A pair of hydrogen atoms clinging together is called a *hydrogen molecule*. We can use an abbreviation for a hydrogen molecule and show that it is made up of two hydrogen atoms by writing H_2.

hydrogen molecule H_2

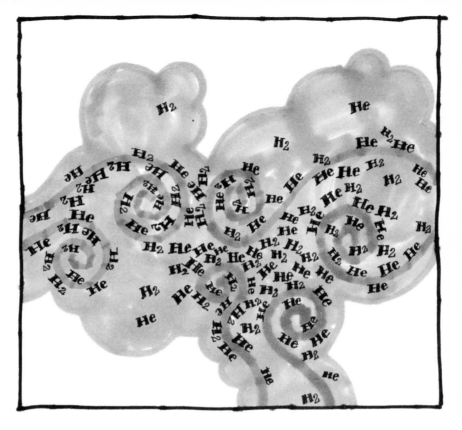

The cloud of gas was cold to begin with and was made up mostly of H_2 and He.

As the cloud came together, it grew hotter and hotter. The atoms and molecules that made it up moved faster and faster. The cloud of gas was hottest at its center and that's where the atoms and molecules were pushed closest together by gravitational pull and where they moved fastest.

As the atoms and molecules moved, they collided with each other and bounced away again. The hotter the cloud, the faster they moved and the harder they collided and bounced. At the center, they collided hardest of all.

For a while, the collisions didn't do much. By the time the center of the cloud reached a temperature of several thousands of degrees, the collisions became violent enough to do damage. Hydrogen molecules began to strike each other so hard that they were shaken apart. The molecules split up into separate atoms. One hydrogen molecule would break up into two hydrogen atoms. We can write that in abbreviated form this way:

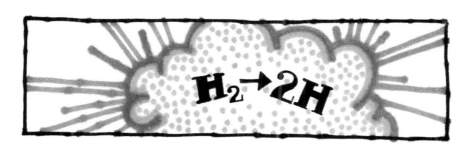

$$H_2 \rightarrow 2H$$

At the center of the developing Sun, then, we would now have a mixture of hydrogen atoms and helium atoms. What happens next as the temperature continues to go up and the atoms collide with greater and greater force?

To answer that, we have to look inside the atom.

The atom is not a little solid ball. It is made up of other, still smaller bits of matter. At the very center of an atom is a tiny object that contains almost all the weight of the atom. This is the *atomic nucleus*. (When we speak of more than one nucleus, we say *nuclei*.)

Whirling around the nucleus, in the outer part of the atom, are very light bits of matter called *electrons*.

The atomic nucleus and the electrons both contain electricity; both have an *electric charge*. The electric charge is of two different kinds.

The atomic nucleus has one kind and the electrons have the other kind. These kinds are labeled *positive* (+) and *negative* (−). The atomic nucleus has a positive electric charge and the electrons have a negative electric charge.

A positive electric charge and a negative electric charge attract each other. That's why the electrons keep circling the atomic nucleus. They are held there by electrical attraction.

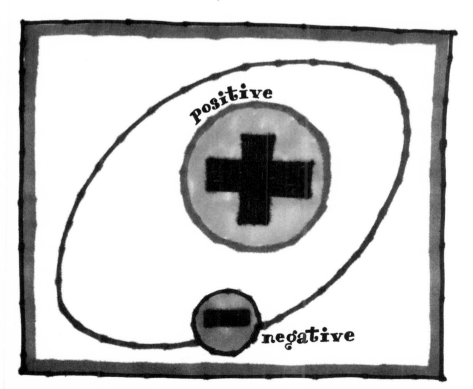

Two objects with positive electric charges or two with negative electric charges push each other away. When two atoms collide, the electrons on the outside of each atom come together. Both sets have negative electric charges and push each other away. That is why atoms bounce off each other when they collide.

The hydrogen atom is the simplest of all atoms. It has one electron and no more. That electron has one negative electric charge. The hydrogen nucleus at the very center of the atom has one positive electric charge.

The atomic nucleus is the more important part of the atom, so we will let it keep the name, hydrogen. We will write the hydrogen nucleus as H^+. The H shows it is hydrogen and the one positive sign ($+$) shows it has one positive electric charge. We can write the electron as e^-. The e stands for electron and the one negative sign ($-$) shows that it has one negative electric charge.

We can write the whole hydrogen atom as:

hydrogen atom

What about the helium atom? It is the second simplest atom. It has two electrons. Each electron has a negative electric charge, so there are two negative electric charges altogether in the atom. We can write the electrons of the helium atom as e^{--}.

The helium nucleus has two positive electric charges. We can write it as He^{++}. The entire helium atom is $He^{++}e^{--}$.

Now let's get back to the center of the cloud of gas that was coming together to form the Sun. The hydrogen atoms and the helium atoms slammed together harder and harder as the temperature kept going up.

Finally, when the temperature rose to a few million degrees, the collisions were so hard that the electrons were knocked right out of the atoms.

Once the electrons are knocked off, the atomic nuclei are bare. They are no longer protected by electrons on the outside. Now the nuclei themselves can start banging together.

By the time the cloud of gas had gotten so hot that the outside was giving off red light, the center was so hot that it was made up of bare hydrogen nuclei and helium nuclei smashing together.

It is the H^+ and the He^{++} that we must now

hydrogen nucleus

think about. Let's take a closer look at them.

The hydrogen nucleus is made up of only one bit of matter. This bit of matter is called a *proton* and it carries the positive electric charge.

The helium nucleus, however, is made up of four tiny bits of matter. Two of them are pro-

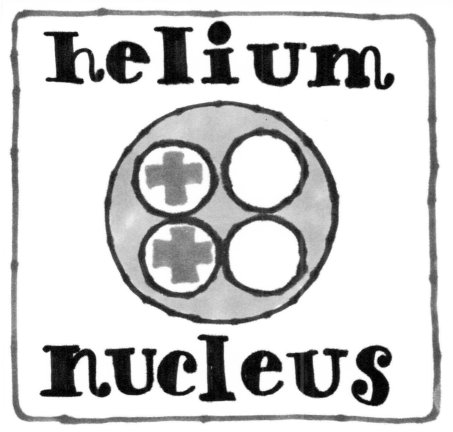

helium nucleus

tons. Each of them has a positive electric charge. That's why the helium nucleus has two positive electric charges altogether. The other two bits of matter are *neutrons*. They are very much like protons but they have no electric charge at all.

Suppose we write the helium nucleus this

He_{oo}^{++}

way, He_{oo}^{++}. The two positive signs $(++)$ represent the two protons and the two signs beneath them (oo) are the two neutrons.

The hydrogen nucleus, made up of just one proton, can still be written as H^+.

hydrogen nucleus

All the nuclei have positive electric charges and they push each other away. When they collide, they therefore bounce apart.

But that depends on how high the temperature is. By the time the temperature is 25,000,000° F., one hydrogen nucleus will strike another one so hard that they will not bounce apart. They will smash together and stick.

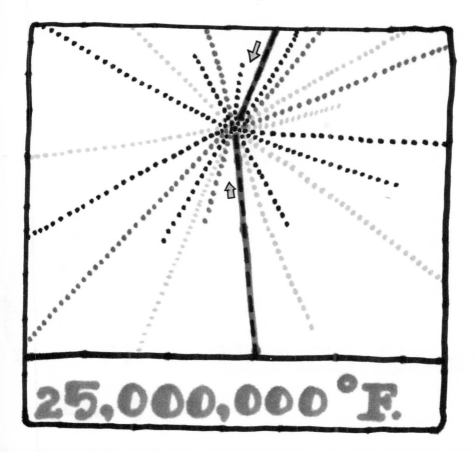

25,000,000°F.

That means two protons are sticking together. One of the protons, however, loses its electric charge and becomes a neutron. Now you have an atomic nucleus made up of one proton and one neutron.

It is the protons that count. As long as a nucleus has a single proton and no more, it is a hydrogen nucleus. It isn't the ordinary kind of hydrogen nucleus, which has just a proton and nothing else. It has a neutron as well. We can write it as H_0^+. This is *heavy hydrogen.*

After the heavy hydrogen nucleus is formed, it keeps on moving about very quickly and smashes against other nuclei. Pretty soon another hydrogen nucleus hits it and sticks. The heavy hydrogen changes into a nucleus that has two protons and one neutron.

Since it has two protons it is now a helium nucleus. It isn't the ordinary kind because it has only one neutron instead of two. We can write it He_0^{++} and we can call it *light helium*.

Finally, one more hydrogen nucleus is added; one more proton which turns into a neutron. That leaves a nucleus with two protons and two neutrons and we have the ordinary helium nucleus He_{oo}^{++}.

The helium nucleus isn't changed any further. The protons and neutrons in a helium nucleus cling together so tightly that even the

smashing collisions at 25,000,000° don't bother it. The temperature has to go much higher before helium nuclei are changed about.

At the temperature of the Sun's center, all that happens, then, is that four hydrogen nuclei are changed into one helium nucleus. We can write that this way:

It so happens that four hydrogen nuclei contain more energy than one helium nucleus. When the four hydrogen nuclei change to a helium nucleus, there is energy left over. Let's write that this way:

$$4H^+ \rightarrow He_{00}^{++} + energy$$

That energy goes boiling out of the Sun as radiation. We can see it as light, when it finally reaches us, and we can feel it as heat.

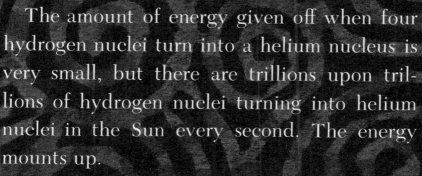

The amount of energy given off when four hydrogen nuclei turn into a helium nucleus is very small, but there are trillions upon trillions of hydrogen nuclei turning into helium nuclei in the Sun every second. The energy mounts up.

If we consider just one pound of hydrogen nuclei turning into helium nuclei, we would find it gives off as much energy as six million pounds of burning gasoline.

one pound of hydrogen nuclei turning into helium nuclei

This explains why the hydrogen bomb is such a terrible weapon. In the hydrogen bomb, some hydrogen nuclei are changed into helium nuclei at very high temperatures, and the energy released produces an enormous explosion.

Well, the Sun is a hydrogen bomb. It is a huge hydrogen bomb that is 860,000 miles across and that has been exploding for billions of years. It doesn't fly apart because its gravitational pull keeps it together—but it keeps exploding.

So now you see what happened. When the original cloud of gas came together, the temperature went up and up and up. Finally, the temperature got high enough to start hydrogen nuclei turning into helium.

That made many times as much energy as was produced just by the atoms of the cloud falling together. Energy from the Sun's center

52

poured out in every direction and warmed the Sun's outside to 10,000° F. and kept it there. From the Sun's outside, energy poured out in all directions into space and some of it reached the Earth.

In order to keep the Sun as hot as it is now, and pouring out as much energy, 650 million tons of hydrogen must turn to helium *every second!*

You might think that this would use up all the hydrogen in the Sun very quickly, but that is not so. The Sun is so enormous that even though it has been using up its hydrogen like this for five billion years, most of the original quantity is still left. There is enough hydrogen left in the Sun right now to keep it shining for at least eight billion years more just as it is doing now.

So we don't have to worry about the Sun. It

will keep on shining, just as it shines today, for day after day, year after year, century after century, for a long, long time.

And in the light and warmth of the good Sun, the Earth will stay the pleasant place it is, if only people take good care of it.

Index and Glossary

atom: stable groupings of protons, neutrons, and electrons. 27–30, 32–39

charge, electric: a property possessed by certain particles which causes them to either attract or repel other particles; two particles whose charges cause them to repel each other are said to have the same charge, two which attract each other have opposite charges. 34–36, 44

    negative charge: the type of electric charge possessed by electrons. 35–36, 37, 38

    positive charge: the type of electric charge possessed by protons. 35–36, 37, 38, 40, 41, 42, 43

electron (e or e^-): the particle in an atom which has the smallest mass, and which has a negative electric charge. 34–35, 36, 37, 38, 39

energy: the property of a body or a system which enables it to do work. 17–19, 20–23, 26, 27, 50–51, 52–54

gravitation: the force which acts on any two particles of matter, whether electrically charged or not, causing each to attract the other. 5–8, 16–17, 19, 20, 30, 33, 52

heat: a form of energy measured by temperature. 19, 20–27, 50 *helium atom* (He or $He^{++}e^{--}$): an atom made up of two protons, two neutrons, and two electrons. 29, 30, 31, 34, 38, 53

helium, light (He_0^{++}): an atom which differs from ordinary helium in that it lacks one neutron. 47

helium nucleus (He^{++} or He_{00}^{++}): the central structure of a helium atom, consisting of two protons and two neutrons. 38, 39, 40, 41–42, 47, 48–50, 51, 52

hydrogen atom (H or H^+e^-): the simplest and smallest atom, made up of one proton and one electron. 29, 30, 31, 34, 36, 37, 38, 53

hydrogen bomb: a military weapon which causes an explosion and release of energy similar to that taking place in the center of the Sun. 52

hydrogen, heavy (H_0^+): an atom which differs from ordinary hydrogen in that it has an added neutron. 45–46

hydrogen molecule (H_2): a tight grouping of a pair of hydrogen atoms. 31, 33

hydrogen nucleus (H^+): the central structure of a hydrogen atom, consisting of a single proton. 36, 37, 39, 40, 42, 43, 45, 48, 49–50, 51, 52

matter: the substance which makes up physical bodies; electrons, neutrons, and protons are among the simplest particles of matter. 13, 16, 17, 19, 27, 34, 40, 41

molecule: a stable grouping of atoms. 31, 32–33

neutron: a particle in the nucleus of an atom; it has no electric charge. 41, 42, 44, 46, 48

nuclei: the plural of nucleus. 34

nucleus, atomic: the central structure of an atom. 34–35, 37, 44–46

planet: one of the bodies now revolving around the Sun, and which formed from the same swirl of gas and at the same time as the Sun. 9–13, 17

proton: a particle in the nucleus of an atom; it has a positive electric charge. 40–41, 42, 44–45, 46–47, 48

radiation: a form in which energy travels with wavelike behavior through space; ordinary visible light is one kind of radiation. 21, 23, 50

   infrared radiation: energy which travels in longer waves than visible light; this radiation is felt as heat. 26

   ultraviolet radiation: energy which travels in shorter waves than visible light; this radiation causes skin tanning. 26

DATE DUE

DATE DUE			
OCT 9 78			
AUG 6 '80			
AUG 6 '85			
APR 2 2 1992			